DR. DOODLE'S CHRISTIAN COMIX

Volume One, Issue Two

ON THE WORD OF GOD

Fred Sanders

ivp

InterVarsity Press
Downers Grove, Illinois

InterVarsity Press® is the book-publishing division of InterVarsity Christian
Fellowship/USA®, a student movement active on campus at hundreds of
universities, colleges and schools of nursing in the United States of America, and a
member movement of the International Fellowship of Evangelical Students. For
information about local and regional activities, write Public Relations Dept.,
InterVarsity Christian Fellowship/USA, 6400 Schroeder Rd., P.O. Box 7895,
Madison, WI 53707-7895.

In most cases Scripture quotations are taken from the *New Revised Standard
Version* of the Bible, copyright 1989 by the Division of Christian Education of the
National Council of the Churches of Christ in the USA. Used by permission. All
rights reserved.

ISBN 0-8308-2242-9

Printed in the United States of America ♾

15 14 13 12 11 10 9 8 7 6 5 4 3 2 1
10 09 08 07 06 05 04 03 02 01 00 99

InterVarsity Press
P.O. Box 1400
Downers Grove, IL 60515

World Wide Web: www.ivpress.com

E-mail: mail@ivpress.com

CONTENTS

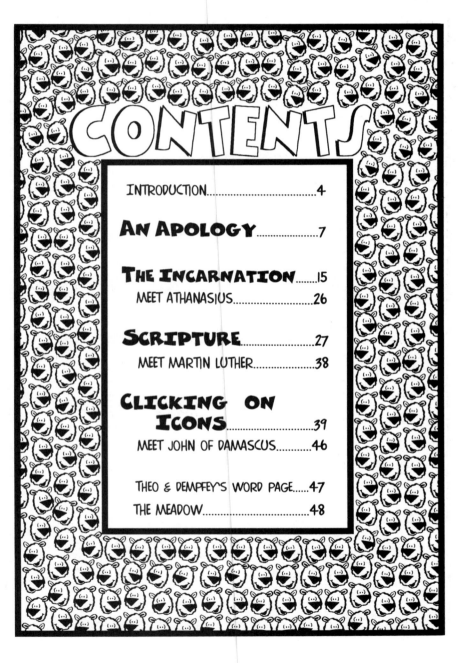

INTRODUCTION

ANOTHER BUSY DAY AT DR. DOCTRINE'S THEOLOGY CLINIC...

IT'S MR. *SCHWARTZ* ON LINE *THREE*, DOC!

PUT HIM THROUGH!

HELLO, SCHWARTZ! WHAT CAN I *DO* FOR YOU?

WHAT?

I SAID, *WHAT* CAN I *DO* FOR YOU?

YES, PLEASE *DO* PUT ME THROUGH.

NO... *THIS IS* DR. DOCTRINE. *WHY* ARE YOU *CALLING?*

OF *COURSE* I CAN TELL THAT YOU'RE *STALLING.* WILL YOU *PLEASE* JUST LET ME TALK TO THE *DOCTOR?*

6

I'M *REAALLLLY* SORRY! I MEAN IT! SO SORRY! I DIDN'T *MEAN* TO BE A CHRISTIAN! BEG YOUR *PARDON!* BOY AM I EMBARASSED! GOSH, I'M REALLY *SORRY!* IT WON'T HAPPEN AGAIN, I *PROMISE!* SORRY!

NO, NO, DEMPFEY, AN *APOLOGY* DOESN'T MEAN APOLOGIZING LIKE THAT. IT MEANS OFFERING A DEFENSE FOR WHAT YOU BELIEVE! *STICKING UP* FOR THE FAITH, NOT *BACKING DOWN* FROM IT!

IN THE SECOND AND THIRD CENTURIES, WHEN CHRISTIANS WERE BEING *PERSECUTED* UNDER THE ROMAN EMPIRE, A LOT OF THEM STARTED WRITING THESE "APOLOGIES" EXPLAINING CHRISTIAN BEHAVIOR AND EVEN PROCLAIMING THE *GOSPEL* IN A WAY THAT THE *ROMANS* COULD HEAR AND UNDERSTAND.

IN THIS ISSUE WE'RE SHARING AN APOLOGY CALLED "THE *EPISTLE TO DIOGNETUS*" --WHICH YOU CAN PRONOUNCE ANY WAY YOU *WANT* TO. NOBODY KNOWS WHO WROTE IT OR *WHO* DIOGNETUS WAS, BUT THE LETTER IS A REAL TREASURE! IT'S A REALLY BEAUTIFUL STATEMENT OF THE CHRISTIAN MESSAGE THAT--

GOSH, I'M SORRY!

DEMPFEY! I JUST GOT THROUGH TELLING YOU THAT AN APOLOGY DOESN'T MEAN--

NO, I *MEAN* IT! I'M SORRY I GOT THE COMIC OFF TO A BAD START! I WANNA *HELP* GET IT BACK ON TRACK!

OH...OKAY! WELL, YOU CAN DO THE BACK-GROUNDS FOR ME. THAT WOULD HELP A LOT!

UH....WELL, WHAT KIND OF BACK-GROUNDS?

YOU KNOW, *ROMAN* STUFF! WHATEVER!

SO HERE'S THE EPISTLE TO *DIOGNETUS!* OH, ONE MORE THING: ONLY *PART* OF IT HAS SURVIVED, SO IT JUST BREAKS OFF AT THE END, WITHOUT REALLY COMING TO A CONCLUSION.

HOPE YOU ENJOY IT!

UM......HEY, WAIT. I'M NOT REAL CLEAR ON THIS "ROMAN STUFF" DEAL...

MY DEAR DIOGNETUS: I SEE THAT YOU ARE SINCERELY *EAGER* TO LEARN ABOUT THE RELIGION OF THE CHRISTIANS. YOU HAVE ASKED ME VERY CLEAR AND CAREFUL *QUESTIONS* ABOUT IT.

WHAT *GOD* DO THEY TRUST? HOW DOES THEIR WORSHIP OF THIS GOD HELP THEM ALL *DISREGARD* THE WORLD AND *DESPISE* DEATH? WHY DO THEY SNEER AT THE SO-CALLED "*GODS*" OF THE GREEKS? WHAT IS THE NATURE OF THIS *LOVE* THEY HAVE FOR EACH OTHER? AND FINALLY, WHY IS IT THAT THIS NEW *RACE*, OR NEW *WAY OF LIFE*, HAS COME INTO BEING IN *OUR* TIME AND NOT EARLIER?

GOOD QUESTIONS!

I'M GLAD YOU'RE SO *EAGER* TO FIND OUT, AND NOW I ASK FOR TWO THINGS FROM *GOD*, WHO GIVES US POWER BOTH TO SPEAK AND TO LISTEN: MAY I *SPEAK* IN SUCH A WAY THAT YOU WILL GET SOME GOOD OUT OF WHAT I SAY, AND MAY YOU BE ENABLED TO *LISTEN* SO WELL THAT I WON'T GO AWAY DISAPPOINTED.

COME ON, THEN, AND *CLEAR AWAY* ANY PREJUDICES THAT CLUTTER YOUR MIND! *THROW OFF* ANY HABIT OF THOUGHT THAT'S LEADING YOU INTO ERROR, AND MAKE A *FRESH START*. YOU HAVE TO BECOME A *NEW PERSON* IF YOU WANT TO HEAR A *NEW STORY!*

DON'T JUST SEE WITH YOUR *EYES* BUT ALSO WITH YOUR *UNDER-STANDING*: WHAT ARE THESE THINGS YOU PEOPLE CALL *GODS*? WHAT ARE THEY *MADE* OF?: STONE, BRONZE, WOOD, SILVER, IRON AND CLAY! THE STUFF WE MAKE ROADS, POTS AND PANS, AND *TOILETS* OUT OF!

THEY'RE DEAF AND BLIND! THEY HAVE NO *SOULS*, NO *SENSE*, NO POWER TO *MOVE!* THEY RUST AND ROT OR GET STOLEN!

YOU CALL THESE THINGS *GODS*; YOU *SERVE* THEM; YOU *BOW DOWN* TO THEM; AND, IN THE END, YOU BECOME *NO BETTER* THAN THEY ARE.

IS *THIS* THE REASON YOU HATE THE CHRISTIANS-- BECAUSE THEY REFUSE TO TAKE THESE *THINGS* FOR *GODS*? I COULD GO ON ALL DAY ABOUT WHY CHRISTIANS REFUSE TO BE *ENSLAVED* TO SUCH "GODS" AS THESE, BUT IF YOU DON'T SEE THE POINT OF WHAT I'VE *ALREADY* SAID, THEN IT WON'T HELP TO SAY ANY MORE.

CHRISTIANS ARE *NO DIFFERENT* FROM EVERYONE ELSE IN NATIONALITY, SPEECH, OR CUSTOMS; THEY DON'T LIVE IN SPECIAL CHRISTIAN *CITIES* OF THEIR OWN, USE A SPECIAL *LANGUAGE* OR ADOPT A PECULIAR WAY OF LIFE. *WHEREVER* THEY HAPPEN TO LIVE, THEY FOLLOW *LOCAL CUSTOMS* REGARDING CLOTHES, FOOD AND SUCH.

STILL, SOMEHOW THEIR WAY OF LIFE REVEALS A *CULTURE*, A SENSE OF *BELONGING*, THAT IS *MARVELOUS* AND --AS EVERYONE ADMITS-- *UNUSUAL*.

THEY'RE *GOOD CITIZENS*, WHEREVER THEY LIVE, BUT SOMEHOW THEY'RE NOT FULLY AT *HOME* ANYWHERE. THEY DO THEIR DUTIES LIKE CITIZENS BUT SUFFER HARDSHIPS LIKE ALIENS.

JUST LIKE ANYONE, THEY GET *MARRIED* AND HAVE KIDS --BUT THEY DON'T *ABANDON* THEIR BABIES. THEY'RE GLAD TO SHARE THEIR *FOOD* --BUT NOT THEIR *BEDS* AND THEIR WIVES!

THEY LIVE ON *EARTH*, BUT THEY ARE *CITIZENS* OF HEAVEN. THEY OBEY THE PUBLIC *LAWS* AND EVEN *EXCEL* THEM IN THEIR PRIVATE LIVES.

THEY *LOVE* EVERYONE BUT ARE *PERSECUTED* BY EVERYONE.

THEY ARE PUT TO *DEATH* YET ARE MORE *ALIVE* THAN EVER.

THEY *LACK* ALL THINGS AND YET IN ALL THINGS THEY *ABOUND*.

THEY ARE *MALIGNED* AND YET ARE *VINDICATED*.

THEY ARE *CURSED* AND YET THEY *BLESS*.

THEY DO *GOOD* YET ARE *PUNISHED* WITH THE WICKED.

AND *WHEN* THEY ARE *PUNISHED* THEY *REJOICE* AS IF THEY WERE GETTING *MORE* OUT OF LIFE.

IN A WORD, WHAT THE *SOUL* IS TO THE *BODY*, *CHRISTIANS* ARE TO THE *WORLD*.

JUST AS THE SOUL IS *LOCKED UP* IN THE BODY AND YET *HOLDS* THE BODY *TOGETHER*, CHRISTIANS ARE HELD IN THE *WORLD* AS IN A *PRISON*, YET IT IS *THEY* WHO HOLD THE WORLD TOGETHER. JUST AS THE IMMORTAL SOUL DWELLS IN A MORTAL TENT, CHRISTIANS ARE PASSING THROUGH TEMPORARY THINGS, BUT THEIR EYES ARE FIXED ON IMMORTALITY IN *HEAVEN*.

JUST AS THE SOUL IS DISTRIBUTED IN *EVERY MEMBER* OF THE BODY, CHRISTIANS ARE SCATTERED IN *EVERY CITY* IN THE WORLD. JUST AS THE SOUL LIVES *IN* THE BODY AND YET IS NOT *PART* OF THE BODY, CHRISTIANS LIVE *IN THE WORLD* BUT ARE NOT *OF THE WORLD*.

PSSST! HEY! I ALREADY *RAN OUT* OF "ROMAN STUFF!" I'M GONNA SORT OF *FAKE IT* FROM HERE ON!

JUST AS THE SOUL IS IMPROVED WHEN IT GOES WITHOUT FOOD AND DRINK, THE NUMBER OF CHRISTIANS *INCREASES* THE MORE THEY ARE *PERSECUTED*.

THIS IS THE ASSIGNMENT *GOD* HAS GIVEN THEM, AND THEY ARE NOT AT LIBERTY TO *DESERT* THIS *POST*.

WHAT IS THE *MESSAGE* THAT'S BEEN COMMITTED TO THEM? IT'S NOT SOME *EARTHLY* DISCOVERY; THEY AREN'T IN THE BUSINESS OF DISPENSING MERELY *HUMAN* MYSTERIES.

THE ALMIGHTY *CREATOR* OF THE UNIVERSE, THE INVISIBLE *GOD* HIMSELF, REACHED DOWN FROM HEAVEN TO PLANT AMONG THEM THE SEED OF *TRUTH*, THE *HOLY WORD* THAT IS MORE THAN HUMAN MINDS CAN COMPREHEND. AND HE MADE IT TAKE *FIRM ROOT* IN THEIR HEARTS.

INSTEAD OF JUST SENDING A **SERVANT** --AN **ANGEL** OF SOME KIND-- HE SENT THE VERY **CREATOR** OF THE **COSMOS**, THE ONE THROUGH WHOM HE CREATED **EVERYTHING!**

THE ONE WHOSE AWESOME **COMMAND** CONTROLS THE ELEMENTS OF **REALITY!** THE **MAKER** AND **SUSTAINER** OF THE SUN, MOON, AND STARS; THE EARTH AND SKY AND SEA! **THIS** IS WHO HE SENT!

AND HE **DIDN'T** SEND HIM --AS MIGHT BE HUMANLY SUPPOSED-- IN ORDER TO **IMPOSE** HIS POWER, TO **TYRANNIZE** AND **TERRORIZE.** CERTAINLY NOT!

HE CAME IN **GENTLENESS** AND **HUMILITY.** HE SENT HIM AS A KING SENDING A **SON.** HE SENT HIM AS **GOD;** HE SENT HIM FOR HUMANITY'S SAKE.

HE SENT HIM TO BE A **SAVIOR,** USING **PERSUASION** INSTEAD OF **BRUTE FORCE** --BECAUSE COERCIVE VIOLENCE IS **NOT** CHARACTERISTIC OF GOD. HE ACTED LIKE SOMEONE INVITING YOU IN, NOT CHASING YOU DOWN; LIKE A **LOVER,** NOT A **JUDGE.**

NOW LATER ON, HE **WILL** SEND HIM AS A JUDGE; AND **THEN** IT'LL BE "KATY, BAR THE DOOR!"

THE CHRISTIANS ARE THROWN TO **WILD ANIMALS** AND TOLD TO **DENY** THEIR LORD, AND YET THEY **REFUSE....**

THE MORE YOU PUNISH THEM, THE MORE THEY **INCREASE....**

DOES THAT LOOK LIKE **HUMAN** ACCOMPLISHMENT TO YOU? NO WAY: THESE THINGS ARE THE **POWER** OF GOD; THEY ARE SIGNS OF **HIS COMING.**

NOW **BEFORE** GOD'S COMING, WHO HAD ANY IDEA WHAT HE WAS **LIKE?** THE GREEK PHILOSOPHERS? **HA!** ONE GROUP OF THEM SAID THAT GOD WAS **FIRE** --WHAT THEY CALL **GOD** IS WHERE THEY'RE LIKELY TO **GO.** ANOTHER GROUP SAID GOD WAS **WATER;** AND SO ON. WELL, LET'S JUST LET **EVERYTHING** BE GOD, WHY DON'T WE? WHAT **NONSENSE!** SHEER **QUACKERY!**

GOD **REVEALED** HIMSELF; APART FROM THAT, NO ONE HAS EVER SEEN OR KNOWN HIM. HE REVEALED HIMSELF BY MEANS OF **FAITH,** AND THAT'S THE ONLY WAY IT'S **POSSIBLE** TO SEE GOD.

AS IT TURNS OUT, GOD IS NOT ONLY A **FRIEND** OF HUMANITY, HE'S ALSO **MERCIFUL!** GOD ALWAYS **WAS** AND ALWAYS **WILL** BE KIND AND GOOD, CALM AND TRUE --ONLY **GOD** IS **THAT** GOOD.

NOW IT *MIGHT* SEEM LIKE GOD DIDN'T *CARE* MUCH ABOUT US BEFORE HE SENT HIS SON...

--LIKE THE *QUESTION* YOU ASKED ME, "WHY DID HE *WAIT* SO LONG?"

WELL, THE POINT IS THAT *NOW* WE ALL KNOW WHAT GOD AND HIS SON KNEW FROM THE *BEGINNING*: GOD HAS SHARED HIS *BLESSINGS* WITH US ALL AT *ONCE* AND LET US SEE THINGS WE COULD *NEVER* HAVE EXPECTED!

AFTER ALL, WHAT DID WE DO WITH ALL THAT *"FREE TIME"* BEFORE GOD'S COMING? WE *CHASED* AFTER WHIMS AND LUSTS AND GOT TOSSED AROUND WITH *NO* CONTROL. THAT WAS *NOT* PART OF GOD'S PLAN! BUT IT SERVED PRETTY WELL TO GET US *READY* FOR THE *PRESENT* ERA OF *HOLINESS*.

AND NOW THAT WE'VE SEEN GOD'S *GOODNESS* AND GRACE --*WOW!* IT'S *INCREDIBLE!* INSTEAD OF HATING US AND *REJECTING* US AND REMEMBERING OUR SINS, HE WAS COMPASSIONATE AND PATIENT, AND TOOK OUR SINS ON *HIMSELF!*

I MEAN, SINCE WE *PROVED* THAT WE WERE UNABLE TO ENTER THE KINGDOM OF GOD ON OUR *OWN* POWER, *NOW* IT'S TIME TO ENTER THE KINGDOM BY THE POWER OF *GOD!*

WHAT A SWEET, *UNEXPECTED* TURN OF EVENTS! WHAT *WE* COULDN'T DO, THE *SAVIOR* DID FOR US; AND NOW WE KNOW THAT GOD IS OUR GUARDIAN, FATHER, TEACHER, ADVISER AND DOCTOR! HE WANTS US TO SEE HIM AS OUR MIND, LIGHT, HONOR, GLORY, STRENGTH AND LIFE, AND NOT TO WORRY ABOUT WHAT WE WEAR AND EAT!

HE GAVE US HIS OWN *SON* FOR OUR *REDEMPTION*. HE GAVE THE HOLY ONE FOR THOSE WHO WERE SINFUL, THE INNOCENT FOR THE WICKED. WHAT *ELSE* BUT HIS *RIGHTEOUSNESS* COULD HAVE BURIED OUR SIN? *WHO* ELSE COULD HAVE *JUSTIFIED* US?

IF *YOU* WANT TO HAVE THIS FAITH, YOU CAN! THE *FIRST* THING YOU NEED IS KNOWLEDGE OF THE *FATHER*. GOD *LOVED* PEOPLE, AND CREATED THE *WORLD* FOR THEIR SAKE.

HE GAVE THEM THEIR *MINDS*; HE MADE THEM IN HIS OWN *IMAGE*. HE SENT HIS ONLY *SON* TO THEM, AND PROMISED THEM THE *KINGDOM OF HEAVEN*, WHICH HE'LL GIVE TO THOSE WHO LOVE HIM. WHEN YOU *UNDERSTAND* THIS, WHAT KIND OF *JOY* DO YOU THINK YOU'LL HAVE? HOW MUCH WILL YOU LOVE THE ONE WHO FIRST LOVED *YOU* SO MUCH?

AND WHEN YOU *LOVE* HIM, YOU WILL BE AN *IMITATOR* OF HIS *GOODNESS*. DON'T BE *SURPRISED* THAT A *HUMAN* CAN IMITATE *GOD*: IT'S POSSIBLE BECAUSE IT'S GOD'S WILL!

THERE'S NO *REAL* HAPPINESS IN *DOMINATING* YOUR NEIGHBORS, IN WANTING TO HAVE *MORE* THAN WEAKER PEOPLE, IN BEING RICH AND ABLE TO *BOSS* YOUR INFERIORS AROUND. *THAT'S* NOT THE WAY TO IMITATE GOD! THOSE THINGS ARE *TOTALLY ALIEN* TO GOD'S GREATNESS.

YOU ARE AN *IMITATOR* OF GOD WHEN YOU TAKE ON YOUR OWN SHOULDERS THE *BURDEN* OF YOUR NEIGHBOR; WHEN YOU CHOOSE TO USE *YOUR* ADVANTAGES TO HELP *ANOTHER* WHO IS UNDERPRIVILEGED; WHEN YOU TAKE WHAT YOU HAVE *RECEIVED* FROM GOD AND *GIVE* TO THOSE WHO ARE IN *NEED*.

--WHEN YOU DO *THIS*, YOU BECOME LIKE *GOD* TO THOSE WHO YOU HELP.

WHEN YOU HAVE *FAITH*, YOU WILL SEE THAT GOD IS IN *HEAVEN* AND *YOU* ARE ON *EARTH*; AND YOU WILL BEGIN TO SPEAK OF THE *MYSTERIES* OF *GOD*, AND YOU'LL KNOW REAL *LIFE* FROM REAL *DEATH*!

INCARNATION

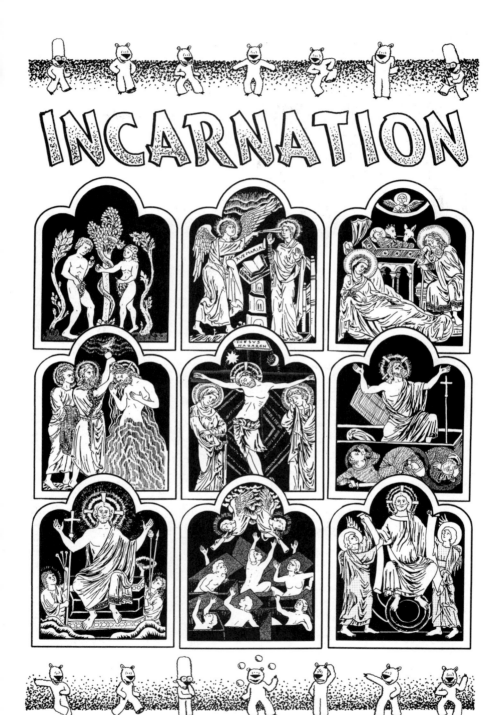

"THE WORD WAS WITH GOD, AND THE WORD WAS GOD... AND THE WORD BECAME FLESH AND LIVED AMONG US."

THE INCARNATION --WHICH MEANS "ENFLESHING," OR "TAKING ON FLESH"-- OF THE SON OF GOD IS ONE OF THE CENTRAL IDEAS OF CHRISTIAN FAITH.

IT TEACHES US THAT WHEN GOD UNDERTOOK TO SAVE US, HE DECIDED TO MAKE IT AN "INSIDE JOB."

THE MORE YOU *THINK* ABOUT THAT, THE MORE YOU REALIZE THAT GOD IS GOOD, *GOOD, GOOD!!* I MEAN, THE FACT THAT HE WAS NOT ONLY WILLING TO *MAKE* BUT ALSO TO *RE-*MAKE THE WHOLE THING... THAT HE JUDGED CREATION TO BE *WORTH* SAVING! *WOW!*

AND --GET THIS-- THAT GOD *KNOWS* WHAT IT'S LIKE TO SEE THINGS FROM *OUR* POINT OF VIEW, BECAUSE JESUS' *HUMANITY* IS A PERMANENT FEATURE OF THE *DIVINE* LIFE.

AND THAT JESUS CHRIST IS AT ONE AND THE SAME TIME THE PERFECT REVELATION OF *GOD'S* NATURE AS WELL AS THE *ONE* REAL EXAMPLE OF *HUMAN* NATURE AS IT WAS MEANT TO BE! *DOUBLE* WOW!

FOR *WOWING* OUT *LOUD!!*

OKAY, I'M GETTING A LITTLE CARRIED AWAY HERE. THAT'S WHY I'VE DECIDED TO STEP ASIDE AND LET A *REAL* PROFESSIONAL DO THE *TEACHING* THIS TIME.

HERE TO PRESENT A SHORTENED VERSION OF HIS GREAT BOOK <u>ON THE INCARNATION</u> IS THAT FAMOUS *PILLAR* OF ORTHODOXY, *DEFENDER* OF THE NICENE CREED, ONE OF *MY* THEOLOGICAL *HEROES* AND AN ALL-AROUND *SWELL* GUY: *ATHANASIUS* OF *ALEXANDRIA!*

Athanasius of Alexandria

LET'S TALK ABOUT THE *INCARNATION* OF THE *WORD* AND HOW HE APPEARED AMONG US. THE FATHER'S WORD DID NOT TAKE ON A BODY BECAUSE OF HIS *OWN* NATURE. BUT IN ORDER TO *SAVE* US. IT WAS ONLY FITTING THAT THE *RENEWAL* OF THE UNIVERSE WAS BROUGHT ABOUT BY THE ONE WHO HAD *CREATED* IT.

GOD CREATED *ALL* THINGS OUT OF *NOTHING!* HE DIDN'T JUST WORK WITH MATERIAL ON HAND, LIKE A CRAFTSMAN; HE CALLED EVERYTHING *INTO BEING* BY HIS OWN POWER AND GAVE IT FORM.

BUT THE *ONE* PART OF CREATION THAT HAD A SHARE IN DIVINE *REASON,* THE *HUMAN RACE,* TURNED FROM GOD, *BREAKING OFF* FELLOWSHIP WITH THE CREATOR. BY DOING THIS THEY TURNED AWAY FROM *LIFE* AND TOWARD THE *NOTHINGNESS* TO WHICH THEY *BELONGED* BY *NATURE.*

WHAT WAS GOD TO DO? THE RACE WAS BEING *DESTROYED;* THE GOOD CREATION WAS PERISHING. WHAT AN *ABSURD* AND *IMPROPER* STATE OF AFFAIRS! IT WOULD HAVE BEEN MORE FITTING FOR HUMANS NEVER TO HAVE BEEN CREATED THAN TO COME INTO BEING AND THEN PERISH LIKE THIS.

WHO COULD UNDO THIS TRAGEDY EXCEPT THE *WORD OF GOD* IN PERSON? ONLY THE ONE WHO *CREATED* THE UNIVERSE WOULD BE ABLE TO *RE-CREATE* IT, SUFFER FOR THE SAKE OF *ALL* AND BE OUR *ADVOCATE* BEFORE THE FATHER.

FOR THIS REASON HE CAME TO OUR REALM --NOT AS IF HE WAS *FAR AWAY* FROM US TO BEGIN WITH! AFTER ALL, HE *FILLS* THE ENTIRE UNIVERSE AND IS ALWAYS PRESENT TO EVERYTHING. BUT OUT OF LOVE HE *CONDESCENDED* TO COME REVEAL HIMSELF TO US.

HE SAW WHAT HAD HAPPENED TO US, HOW CORRUPTION AND NON-EXISTENCE HAD GAINED A *HOLD* OVER OUR LIVES. SO HE DIDN'T JUST APPEAR TO US AS A *VISION* OF SOME KIND. NO, HE TOOK ON A HUMAN *BODY* LIKE OURS AND *SUBJECTED* HIMSELF TO THE SAME DEGRADATION WE FACE. *SURRENDERING* HIMSELF TO *DEATH* ON OUR BEHALF, HE OFFERED HIS BODY AS A *SACRIFICE* TO THE FATHER.

THE WORD TOOK ON A BODY THAT COULD *DIE*, AND THAT BODY BECAME *INCORRUPTIBLE* BECAUSE OF THE *WORD* DWELLING IN IT!

18

IT'S LIKE WHEN A *KING* MOVES INTO A CITY AND TAKES UP *RESIDENCE* IN ONE OF THE ORDINARY HOUSES IN IT. THE *ENEMY* DOESN'T DARE TO *ATTACK* THE CITY, OR *ANY* OF ITS HOUSES, BECAUSE THE KING HIMSELF IS DWELLING IN *ONE* OF THEM.

OR IT'S LIKE WHEN A KING BUILDS A CITY AND *VANDALS* BREAK IN TO DESTROY IT: HE DOESN'T JUST *LET* THEM. HE *RESCUES* HIS WORK! HE DOESN'T *NEGLECT* THE CITY JUST BECAUSE THE INHABITANTS WERE *NEGLIGENT* ABOUT DEFENDING IT; HE *ACTS* ON ITS BEHALF!

TRULY THIS *GREAT RESCUE* IS IN KEEPING WITH THE *GOODNESS* OF *GOD!* THE INCARNATION OF GOD THE WORD BROUGHT ABOUT THE *OVERTHROW* OF DEATH AND THE *RESURRECTION* OF LIFE. NOW WE NO LONGER DIE AS THOSE WHO ARE *CONDEMNED*, BUT AS THOSE WHO WILL *RISE AGAIN*.

19

HERE'S ANOTHER WAY OF LOOKING AT THE SAME THING: TO *GUARANTEE* THAT HUMANS WOULD NEVER BE WITHOUT *KNOWLEDGE* OF GOD, HE GAVE US THE *DIGNITY* OF BEING CREATED ACCORDING TO HIS *IMAGE*.

AND WHAT DID WE DO WITH IT? IMMEDIATELY WE STARTED WORSHIPING *IDOLS*. WE *IGNORED* THE TRUE GOD AND WIPED AWAY *ALL* KNOWLEDGE OF HIM. THE IMAGE OF GOD BECAME UTTERLY *UNRECOGNIZABLE*.

WHAT WAS GOD TO DO? HE TOOK UP THE *CAUSE* OF HIS CREATURES AND SENT HIS OWN *TRUE IMAGE* TO DWELL AMONG THEM. I MEAN HIS *SON*, THE *WORD*, THE *IMAGE* OF THE INVISIBLE *GOD*.

IMAGINE A *PORTRAIT* THAT GETS COMPLETELY WIPED AWAY. HOW COULD IT BE *RE-PAINTED* ACCURATELY? ONLY IF THE *SUBJECT* COMES AND *POSES* AGAIN FOR A RE-PAINTING. *THAT'S* WHAT GOD HAD TO DO: HE SENT HIS *TRUE IMAGE* TO *RESTORE* KNOWLEDGE OF GOD ON EARTH.

JESUS CHRIST, THE ULTIMATE *TEACHER*, CAME TO SHOW US GOD IN A WAY *PERFECTLY* SUITED TO BREAK THROUGH OUR WEAKNESS AND *DISTRACTIBILITY*.

WHY DID THIS TEACHER HAVE TO **DIE?** BECAUSE HE DIDN'T COME JUST TO **TELL US** THINGS BUT TO ACTUALLY **CHANGE** OUR MISERABLE SITUATION. SO AFTER **PROVING** THAT HE WAS THE TRUE IMAGE OF GOD BY HIS PERFECT LIFE AND HIS MIRACLES, HE SURRENDERED HIS BODY TO **DEATH** ON BEHALF OF ALL.

HE DIED IN **PUBLIC** SO NO ONE COULD **DOUBT** HIS DEATH. HE DIED RAISED UP **IN THE AIR** TO OPEN THE WAY TO **HEAVEN,** AND HE DIED WITH HIS **ARMS** SPREAD APART TO **REACH OUT** AND **DRAW** ALL PEOPLE TO HIMSELF.

BUT WHY SUCH A VIOLENT, **SHAMEFUL** DEATH? BECAUSE THE LORD WAS LIKE A CHAMPION **FIGHTER** WHO DOESN'T CHOOSE HIS **OWN** OPPONENTS, LEST EVERYONE THINKS HE'S PICKING THE **EASIEST** FIGHTS. HE DIDN'T CONTRIVE HIS OWN DEATH BUT ACCEPTED THE **WORST** KIND THAT COULD BE THROWN AT HIM: THE **CROSS!**

THE INCARNATE **WORD** DID **TWO** THINGS AT ONCE: HE ACCEPTED THE FULL FORCE OF **DEATH** IN HIS **BODY,** AND HE **DESTROYED** DEATH AND CORRUPTION, BECAUSE **THAT** BODY BELONGED TO THE **WORD** OF GOD!

AND JESUS CHRIST THE WORD IS *LIVING* AND *ACTIVE* TODAY, CENTURIES LATER.

HOW DO WE *KNOW* HE'S ALIVE?

WELL, *DEAD MEN* TEND TO *HOLD STILL.* JESUS, ON THE OTHER HAND, IS DEMONSTRABLY *BUSY* IN THE WORLD: HE IS CHASING AWAY FALSE GODS, CASTING OUT DEMONS, GUIDING PEOPLE TO VIRTUE, REVEALING GOD THE FATHER AND FREEING HIS FOLLOWERS FROM THE FEAR OF DEATH.

HE *SPURS* THE SLOTHFUL TO DO GOOD WORKS, AND HE *STOPS* BUSY SINNERS IN THEIR TRACKS! THIS IS *NOT* THE BEHAVIOR WE EXPECT FROM A *DEAD MAN!*

YOU MAY NOT *SEE* HIM, BUT HIS *POWER* IS ALL AROUND YOU. MAYBE YOU HAVEN'T LOOKED DIRECTLY AT THE *SUN* TODAY, BUT YOU KNOW IT'S *THERE* BECAUSE YOU FEEL ITS *HEAT* AND SEE ITS *LIGHT* EVERYWHERE YOU LOOK.

HE IS CLEARLY THE *SON OF GOD:* WHAT MERE *MAN* OR *MAGICIAN* OR *TYRANT* OR *KING* EVER ACCOMPLISHED SO MUCH? *WHO ELSE* EVER DID BATTLE AGAINST ALL *IDOLATRY,* THE WHOLE HOST OF *DEMONS* AND *MAGIC,* AND ALL THE *WISDOM* OF THE ALMIGHTY GREEKS --AND OVERTHREW EVERY ONE OF THEM ALL AT ONCE? WHO ELSE BUT *OUR LORD,* THE TRUE *WORD OF GOD?*

JESUS CHRIST THE WORD TOOK ON A BODY, TAUGHT THE WORLD ABOUT *GOD,* DESTROYED *DEATH* AND GAVE ETERNAL *LIFE* TO ALL THROUGH THE PROMISE OF THE *RESURRECTION.*

AS THE *FIRST EXAMPLE* OF RESURRECTED LIFE HE RAISED UP HIS *OWN* BODY AND SHOWED IT AS A *TROPHY* OVER THE POWER OF DEATH, *CONQUERING* BY THE SIGN OF THE CROSS.

WELL, I DON'T HAVE *TIME* OR *SPACE* TO SHARE ANY MORE THAN THIS BARE *OUTLINE* OF OUR FAITH IN CHRIST AND HIS INCARNATION. YOU SHOULD TAKE *EVERY* OPPORTUNITY TO STUDY THE *SCRIPTURES* AND LEARN ALL THE REST.

BUT *REMEMBER* AS YOU STUDY THE BIBLE, IF YOU REALLY WANT TO *LEARN* FROM IT, YOU NEED TO HAVE A GOOD *LIFE*, A PURE *SOUL* AND *VIRTUE* IN CHRIST. INTELLECTUAL *KNOWLEDGE* OF THE WORD IS NOT ENOUGH; WHAT MATTERS IS TO *APPROACH* GOD AND WASH YOUR SINS AWAY, *COMMITTING* YOUR LIFE TO GOD THE FATHER IN JESUS CHRIST OUR LORD.

THERE YOU'LL LEARN ABOUT HIS *SECOND* COMING, NOT IN HUMBLE *HIDDENNESS* THIS TIME BUT IN *OPEN GLORY*; NOT TO *SUFFER* BUT TO EXTEND THE RESURRECTION TO ALL AND TO *JUDGE* EVERY PERSON ON EARTH.

NOW TO GOD THE *FATHER*, WITH THE *SON*, IN THE *HOLY SPIRIT* BE HONOR AND POWER AND GLORY, FOR EVER AND EVER. *AMEN.*

MEET THE THEOLOGIANS

ATHANASIUS OF ALEXANDRIA

296-373

ATHANASIUS, BISHOP OF ALEXANDRIA, IS ONE OF THE MOST IMPORTANT THEOLOGIANS IN HISTORY. HE WAS VERY POPULAR AS A PASTOR IN HIS CITY BUT EXTREMELY UNPOPULAR WITH A WHOLE SERIES OF ROMAN EMPERORS. HE WAS SENT INTO EXILE FIVE TIMES --FOR 17 OF HIS 46 YEARS AS A BISHOP!

> *GOD* HIRED ME, SO YOU CAN'T FIRE ME!

A LEGEND ABOUT HIS CHILDHOOD SAYS THAT ONCE WHILE PLAYING IN THE RIVER NEAR THE CHURCH, HE PERFORMED A MOCK BAPTISM ON TWO OF HIS LITTLE FRIENDS. BISHOP ALEXANDER WAS PASSING BY AND CAUGHT HIM IN THE ACT. AFTER A STRICT ROUND OF QUESTIONING, THE BISHOP WAS CONVINCED THAT THESE "FAKE" BAPTISMS WERE SO WELL ADMINISTERED THAT HE VALIDATED THEM! HE BAPTIZED YOUNG ATHANASIUS HIMSELF, MAKING A TOTAL OF THREE CONVERTS THAT DAY. LATER ATHANASIUS BECAME THE BISHOP'S ASSISTANT AND FINALLY SUCCEEDED HIM.

AS THE BISHOP'S ASSISTANT, ATHANASIUS WAS PRESENT AT THE COUNCIL OF NICEA IN 325. THIS COUNCIL REJECTED THE HERESY OF ARIANISM, WHICH DENIED THAT JESUS WAS DIVINE. EVEN THOUGH THEY WERE REFUTED BY THE COUNCIL THE FOLLOWERS OF ARIUS KEPT SPREADING THEIR IDEAS AND CAUSING TROUBLE. SOME OF THE ARIANS WERE BRILLIANT AND POWERFUL DEBATERS, AND ATHANASIUS HAD TO BECOME JUST AS SKILLFUL IN ORDER TO BREAK THROUGH THEIR ARGUMENTS AND SHOW THEIR IDEAS TO BE NON-CHRISTIAN.

> OH, I THINK JESUS IS JUST SUPER! HE'S SORT OF A SUPER-MAN. IN FACT, HE'S A *GOD*, A VERY MIGHTY GOD.

> CLOSE, BUT NO SAVIOR.

ATHANASIUS WAS GOOD AT SEEING THE BIG PICTURE, AND HE COULD COMPROMISE ON DETAILS TO HELP KEEP THE PEACE. BUT WHEN IT CAME TO THE CENTRAL TRUTHS OF CHRISTIAN FAITH, HE DUG IN HIS HEELS TO TAKE A STAND AGAINST THE WHOLE WORLD: "ATHANASIUS AGAINST THE WORLD" IS A PHRASE OFTEN USED TO DESCRIBE HIM. WHEN THE ARIANS SAID JESUS WAS "LIKE GOD," (IN GREEK, THAT'S HOMO IOUSIOS), ATHY INSISTED THAT JESUS IS OF THE SAME ESSENCE AS GOD (GREEK, HOMOOUSIOS). YES, HE FOUGHT TO THE BITTER END OVER ONE ITTY BITTY GREEK LETTER.

> OH JUST COOPERATE! THERE'S NO "I" IN *"TEAM."*

> WELL, THERE'S NO "I" IN "HOMOOUSIOS" EITHER! BUT THERE'S ONE IN *"HERETIC!"*

> AND THERE'S *TWO* IN "EXCOMMUNICATION!"

> AND "NITWIT!"

ATHANASIUS' MOST FAMOUS BOOK IS <u>ON THE INCARNATION OF THE WORD</u>. HE WAS THE FIRST THINKER TO TAKE THE STORY OF JESUS CHRIST AND RE-TELL IT WITH ALL OF ITS IMPLICATIONS FOR HOW WE THINK ABOUT CREATION, THE FALL, SIN, WHAT IT MEANS TO BE HUMAN, AND SO ON. THE WAY ATHANASIUS TELLS THE STORY, JESUS IS THE UNIQUE, ETERNAL SON OF GOD WHO CAME INTO OUR WORLD TO FREE US FROM OUR BONDAGE TO SIN AND SET US FREE TO BECOME CREATED SONS AND DAUGHTERS OF GOD. THIS IS WHY ATHANASIUS FOUGHT SO DOGGEDLY FOR DOCTRINES: OUR SALVATION WAS AT STAKE! JESUS HAD TO BE WHO HE WAS TO HAVE DONE WHAT HE DID!

> WHAT HE *DID* AND WHAT HE *CONTINUES* TO DO NOW!

ATHANASIUS DID SO MANY OTHER IMPORTANT THINGS THAT IT'S HARD TO RECOUNT THEM ALL: HE DEFENDED THE DIVINITY OF THE HOLY SPIRIT JUST AS VIGOROUSLY AS HE DID THAT OF JESUS; HE WROTE A BIOGRAPHY OF SAINT ANTHONY THAT HELPED START THE MONASTIC MOVEMENT; HE KEPT THE CHURCH FROM BEING TAKEN OVER BY THE STATE; HE WAS THE FIRST PERSON TO MAKE A LIST OF ALL 27 BOOKS IN THE NEW TESTAMENT CANON; AND HE SHOWED THE NEXT GENERATION OF THEOLOGIANS HOW TO BE MORE CRITICAL AND CAREFUL IN THEIR USE OF GREEK PHILOSOPHY. HIS RICH TRINITARIAN VISION OF CHRISTIAN FAITH HAS INSPIRED CENTURIES OF BELIEVERS.

> *WHY* DID THE WORD BECOME FLESH? TO BE THE PERFECT HUMAN RECIPIENT OF THE *SPIRIT*. BECAUSE HE RECEIVED THE SPIRIT ON OUR BEHALF, *WE* CAN NOW BE FILLED WITH THE SPIRIT OF ADOPTION, TO THE *GLORY* OF *GOD* THE FATHER!

ASK DR. DOCTRINE

I PRESCRIP SCRIBETURE!

I MEAN, I PRESCRIBE SCRIPTURE!

DEAR DOC, DOES THE BIBLE SAY THAT RABBITS CHEW CUD, AND DO THEY REALLY?

GOOD QUESTION!

YES, LEVITICUS 11:6 SAYS THAT "THE *HARE* CHEWETH *CUD*," AND TO ANSWER THE *REST* OF THE QUESTION, HERE'S MY PAL, *HAREY!*

HI GANG! FIRST OF ALL, LEVITICUS TALKS ABOUT *HARES*, NOT *RABBITS!* WE HARES ARE *BIGGER* AND *COOLER* THAN RABBITS!

NOW, DO WE CHEW CUD? NO, NOT REALLY! TO ACT-UALLY "*RUMINATE*," IT TAKES *FOUR* STOMACHS! THAT WAY, YOU CAN *ROTATE* THE FOOD, CHEWING AND DIGESTING IT AGAIN!

CUD GEAR

WE HARES *DON'T* HAVE FOUR STOMACHS! BUT WE *DO* SIT AROUND WIGGLING OUR *NOSES*, SO IT KIND OF *LOOKS* LIKE WE'RE CHEWING ALL THE TIME!

PRETTY *CUTE* OF US, HUH?

AND THEN THERE'S THIS THING WE DO CALLED "*REFECTING*." IT'S WHERE YOU, UM, YOU KNOW, CHEW THE FOOD *TWICE* BY, UM.... WELL, PASSING IT THROUGH THE SYSTEM AND THEN

THANK YOU, HAREY! YOU DID *FINE*; I'LL TAKE OVER NOW!

BUT... I'M EXPLAINING HOW COME THE BIBLE CAN SAY "HARES CHEW CUD..."

WELL, SERIOUSLY, HAREY, LEVITICUS ISN'T ABOUT FOUR *STOMACHS* AND --UGH-- *REFECTION!* IT'S NOT A *BIOLOGY* TEXTBOOK, IT'S A *FIELD GUIDE* TO SHOW ISRAELITES WHICH ANIMALS TO EAT!

I WAS JUST TRYING TO HELP...

YOU DID *GREAT!* I'M JUST SAYING THAT, INSTEAD OF WASTING TIME TRYING TO MAKE THE BIBLE SAY WHAT WE *THINK* IT SHOULD SAY, WE SHOULD *READ* IT AS IT *ASKS* TO BE READ!

YOU MEAN WE SHOULD, LIKE, *RUMINATE* ON IT?

EXACTLY! THAT'S MY ANSWER!

29

TO SAY IT AS CONCISELY AS POSSIBLE: THE *BIBLE* IS THE *WORD* OF *GOD*.

WHEN WE SAY THAT, WE'RE SAYING A *LOT* OF VERY IMPORTANT THINGS IN ONE SHORT FORMULA. SO LET'S *UNPACK* THAT FORMULA AND SEE *HOW MUCH* IT MEANS. "WORD OF GOD" CAN MEAN *THREE* THINGS TO US.

FIRST OF ALL, GOD'S *WORD* IS WHAT GOD *SAYS* WHEN HE *SPEAKS*.

WORD

WORDS COMING FROM HERE

THINK OF HOW IN THE OLD TESTAMENT GOD'S WORD HAS TO DO WITH GOD SPEAKING *OUT LOUD, ORALLY*, RATHER THAN WRITING THINGS DOWN. GOD *SPEAKS*-- AND THE WORLD IS *CREATED*, OR CEDARS *BREAK*, OR NATIONS *TREMBLE!*

BLA BLA BLA!

"GOD'S SPEECH" IS A WAY OF TALKING ABOUT GOD *DOING* THINGS, AND GOD'S *WORD* IS EXACTLY THAT: *GOD IN ACTION!*

SECONDLY, WHEN GOD TOOK HIS MOST RADICAL, *DECISIVE* ACTION BY SENDING HIS *SON*, HE WAS *EXPRESSING* HIS *CHARACTER*, HIS *LOVE*, AND HIS *HOLINESS* TO THE FULLEST EXTENT POSSIBLE.

THAT'S WHY JOHN CALLS JESUS THE *WORD*: IN THE BEGINNING WAS THE WORD, AND THE WORD BECAME FLESH AND LIVED AMONG US. WHAT GOD HAS TO SAY, HE SAYS TO US IN *JESUS!*

30

31

NOW, IF *CHRIST* IS GOD'S WORD, AND THE *BIBLE* IS GOD'S WORD, THEN WE CAN USE A HANDY *ANALOGY* BETWEEN THE TWO OF THEM:

JUST AS *JESUS* IS FULLY HUMAN AND FULLY GOD, SO IS THE *BIBLE!* THAT IS, THE BIBLE HAS A *HUMAN* NATURE AND A *DIVINE* NATURE!

AND SINCE JESUS HAS TWO NATURES, IT'S POSSIBLE TO MAKE *TWO* MAIN *MISTAKES* ABOUT HIM:

YOU CAN IGNORE HIS *DIVINE* NATURE AND MAKE HIM JUST ANOTHER PERSON, ONE WHO LIVED A GOOD LIFE AND TAUGHT FINE IDEAS.

OR YOU CAN IGNORE HIS HUMANITY, WHICH WOULD MAKE HIM SOME KIND OF *TRICK* THAT GOD WAS PLAYING ON US WHERE HE JUST *PRETENDED* TO BE ONE OF US.

DIVINE

HUMAN

WELL, YOU CAN DO THE *SAME* THING WITH THE BIBLE: ON THE *ONE* HAND, YOU CAN TREAT IT LIKE JUST ANY OTHER *BOOK.* THAT WOULD BE MISSING THE POINT!

MOBY DICK

PASSION'S FURY

THE BIBLE

TOM CLANCY

HO HUM!

ON THE *OTHER* HAND, YOU CAN PRETEND IT *FELL* OUT OF *HEAVEN* ONE DAY, WRITTEN BY THE FINGER OF GOD, COMPLETELY *UNTOUCHED* BY HUMAN HANDS!

BOTH MIS-READINGS ARE *EQUALLY* WRONG!

33

34

IN *ALL* OF THESE WAYS THAT GOD HAS CHOSEN TO *SPEAK* HIS WORD AND TO *INSPIRE* ITS RE-CORDING, THE *HUMAN* NATURE OF THE BIBLE COMES THROUGH CLEARLY.

TO BE PRECISE, THE *PER-SONALITIES* OF THE INDIVIDUAL *WRITERS* AND *BOOKS* COME THROUGH. WE HEAR *EACH* OF THEIR VOICES DISTINCTLY, BUT WE *ALSO* HEAR THE *UNITY* OF THEIR VOICES *TOGETHER*.

IT'S AS IF THEY'RE AN *ORCHESTRA*, AND THEY EACH PLAY THEIR OWN DISTINCTIVE *INSTRU-MENTS* AND *PARTS*.

IN THE NEW TESTAMENT ORCHESTRA, LET'S SAY THE *GOSPELS* ARE THE *STRINGS*, PLAYING A CLEAR NARRATIVE MELODY. *PAUL* IS THE *BRASS* SECTION, SOME-TIMES STATING THE THEMES AS CLEARLY AS A *TRUMPET!* YOU GET THE IDEA!

TO *FULLY* APPRECIATE THE BIBLE YOU NEED TO BE ABLE TO HEAR THE *SEPARATE* PARTS BEING PLAYED ON THE SEPARATE INSTRUMENTS, SO THEN YOU CAN HEAR *HOW WELL* THEY *BLEND* TOGETHER.

SO THAT'S *PART* OF WHAT WE MEAN WHEN WE CALL THE BIBLE GOD'S WORD: IT'S THE INSPIRED *RECORD* OF GOD'S DEALINGS WITH HIS PEOPLE; IT'S THE ILLUMINATED MANUSCRIPT THAT *LIGHTS UP* OUR PATH; IT'S THE *SWORD* OF THE *SPIRIT*; AND A RICH *SYMPHONIC* REVELATION OF GOD'S *CHARACTER* AND *WILL!*

BUT NOW THAT WE'VE SAID ALL THAT, WE NEED TO *REMIND* OURSELVES OF ONE THING: GOD DIDN'T GIVE US THE BIBLE JUST SO WE COULD SAY *NICE THINGS* ABOUT IT. THAT'S *CHEAP* AND *EASY!*

SURE, WE'VE *SAID* ALL THE RIGHT THINGS ABOUT IT, BUT WHAT'S *MORE* IMPORTANT IS, HAVE YOU *READ* THE BIBLE? ARE YOU *READ-ING* THE BIBLE? ARE YOU ESTABLISHING A LIFESTYLE OF *GROW-ING* IN THE WORD AND *OBEYING* IT?

MEDIEVAL ARTISTS *PAINTED* EACH PAGE OF THE BIBLE, "ILLUMINATING" THE MANUSCRIPT WITH PICTURES AND DESIGNS. WHY? TO *SYMBOL-IZE* THE *BEAUTY* AND *RICHNESS* WHICH THEY KNEW AND EXPERIENCED IN *GOD'S WORD*. CAN *YOU* DO THE SAME WITH *YOUR* BIBLE?

SURE THING!

WAIT, HAREY, IT'S A *METAPHOR!*

THE REAL POINT IS TO *READ* AND *USE* IT: "APPLY *YOURSELF* COMPLETELY TO THE *BIBLE,* AND APPLY THE *BIBLE* COMPLETELY TO *YOURSELF!*"

MEET THE THEOLOGIANS

MARTIN LUTHER

1483-1546

MARTIN LUTHER WAS MISTER PROTESTANT REFORMATION. HIS PERSONAL SEARCH FOR THE ANSWER TO THE QUESTION "HOW DO I FIND A GRACIOUS GOD?" TOUCHED OFF THE WHOLE MOVEMENT OF REFORM THAT CHANGED THE COURSE OF HISTORY IN THE CHRISTIAN WEST. HIS ANSWER TO THAT QUESTION REMAINS THE CLASSIC PROTESTANT ANSWER: IN SCRIPTURE ALONE, THROUGH FAITH ALONE, BY GRACE ALONE.

EARLY IN HIS LIFE, LUTHER SAW A PICTURE OF JESUS IN A LOCAL CHURCH, AND IT HAUNTED HIM FOR YEARS: THIS JESUS WAS A STERN JUDGE, SEATED ON A RAINBOW, WITH SWORDS OF CONDEMNATION COMING OUT OF HIS MOUTH. "THE RIGHTEOUSNESS OF GOD" SEEMED TO LUTHER TO MEAN THAT THIS HARSH LAWGIVER WAS POISED TO STRIKE HIM DOWN FOR HIS SINS. AFTER YEARS OF MISERY, IT DAWNED ON LUTHER THAT IN THE BIBLE "GOD'S RIGHTEOUSNESS" REALLY MEANS THE LOVE OF GOD WHICH MAKES US RIGHTEOUS! THIS WAS TRULY GOOD NEWS TO LUTHER.

ON THE ONE HAND, LUTHER BELIEVED IN THE GOSPEL THAT TOLD HIM GOD HAD PROCLAIMED HIM RIGHTEOUS IN CHRIST. BUT ON THE OTHER HAND, LUTHER HAD ONE OF THE MOST POWERFUL, HARDWORKING, GUILT-MONGERING CONSCIENCES IN THE HISTORY OF THE WORLD: HE KNEW THAT EVERY DAY HE COMMITTED SINS. LUTHER DECIDED THAT THE ONLY WAY TO BE TRUE TO THE GOSPEL WAS TO LIVE WITH THAT TENSION BETWEEN BOTH TRUTHS: THE CHRISTIAN MUST BE AT ONE TIME BOTH JUSTIFIED AND ALSO A PERSON WHO SINS.

WELL, *EXCUSE* ME!

IN ALL THE CONFLICTS AND PROJECTS HE WAS INVOLVED IN DURING HIS EVENTFUL LIFE, LUTHER TOOK HIS BEARINGS FROM THE PRINCIPLE THAT GOD'S WORD IS ABSOLUTELY SOVEREIGN: WE CANNOT CONTROL IT, MASTER IT, PARCEL IT OUT OR TURN IT INTO A COMMODITY. GOD SPEAKS WHEN AND WHERE HE CHOOSES TO, AND IS UNDER NO CONSTRAINT FROM US. LUTHER COMPARED THE SENDING OF THE WORD TO "A MOVING RAIN-SHOWER," WHICH CAN DRENCH ONE SPOT WHILE LEAVING ANOTHER COMPLETELY DRY.

BASED ON PSALM 119, LUTHER TAUGHT THAT THERE ARE THREE THINGS YOU NEED TO BE A GOOD THEOLOGIAN. FIRST IS PRAYER, ESPECIALLY PRAYER FOR ENLIGHTENMENT BY THE HOLY SPIRIT. SECOND, YOU MUST HAVE THE PERSONAL EXPERIENCE OF BEING ASSAILED BY TEMPTATIONS AND TRIALS, SO THAT YOU CAN KNOW WHAT IT MEANS TO BE COMFORTED BY GOD'S WORD. THIRD IS MEDITATION, OR DWELLING ON THE WORDS OF SCRIPTURE AT LENGTH, READING THEM ALOUD WITH DILIGENT ATTENTION.

TAKE CARE THAT YOU DO NOT GROW WEARY WHEN YOU HAVE READ, HEARD OR SPOKEN THE WORDS ONCE OR TWICE: YOU WILL NEVER BE A PARTICULARLY GOOD THEOLOGIAN IF YOU DO THAT. GOD WILL NOT GIVE YOU HIS SPIRIT WITHOUT THE EXTERNAL WORD; SO TAKE YOUR CUE FROM THAT.

LUTHER COULD ALWAYS BE COUNTED ON FOR A GOOD DOWN-TO-EARTH ANALOGY. ONCE WHILE HE WAS EATING DINNER WITH FRIENDS AND FAMILY, HIS PUPPY CAME TO THE TABLE AND SAT TRANSFIXED, STARING "WITH OPEN MOUTH AND MOTIONLESS EYES" AT THE FOOD LUTHER WAS ABOUT TO PUT IN HIS MOUTH. LUTHER POINTED TO HIM AND SIGHED, "OH, IF I COULD ONLY PRAY THE WAY THAT DOG WATCHES THE MEAT!"

CLICKING ON

ICONS

FOR *MOST* PEOPLE THESE DAYS, "*ICON*" MEANS THAT LITTLE IMAGE ON YOUR *COMPUTER* THAT YOU DOUBLE-CLICK ON TO START A PROGRAM.

--AN ITTY-BITTY THUMBNAIL DRAWING THAT REPRESENTS THE APPLICATION YOU WANT.

BUT IN THE *EASTERN ORTHODOX* CHURCH "*ICON*" MEANS *MUCH MORE* THAN THAT! FOR EASTERN CHRISTIANS, ICONS ARE AN *IMPORTANT* PART OF THEIR *SPIRITUAL LIFE!*

TO HELP *EXPLAIN* WHAT ICONS MEAN IN THE ORTHODOX TRADITION I'VE INVITED *JOHN OF DAMASCUS* --AN EIGHTH-CENTURY THEOLOGIAN AND A *BIG* FAN OF ICONS-- TO SHARE HIS THOUGHTS WITH US.

WELCOME TO THE COMIC BOOK, *JOHN!*

PLEASED TO *BE* HERE. I BEG THE ALMIGHTY *GOD*, BEFORE WHOM *ALL* THINGS LIE OPEN, TO *BLESS* THE WORDS OF MY MOUTH.

WOW. OKAY, THEN.

UH-HUH. THEY'RE REAL *HEAD-TURNERS.*

AND ICONS ARE ALSO A POWERFUL *EDUCATIONAL* TOOL! I MEAN, IT'S *ONE* THING TO HEAR THE STORIES OF THE BIBLE OVER AND OVER, BUT IT REALLY HELPS WHEN YOU *SEE* THEM AND GET THE *IMAGE* OF THE EVENTS IN FRONT OF YOU.

JUST AS *WORDS* SPEAK TO THE *EAR*, THE *ICON* SPEAKS TO THE *SIGHT*. IT BRINGS US UNDERSTANDING. THE HOLY IMAGES BRING THE PURE *DOCTRINE* BEFORE OUR *EYES*.

YUP.

AND YOU HAVE TO ADMIT, THESE THINGS ARE REALLY EMOTIONALLY *MOVING*. I MEAN, THERE'S JUST SOMETHING ABOUT *SEEING* THESE SERIOUS *FACES* AND THE *EVENTS* THAT ARE PORTRAYED...

THE HOLY IMAGES SERVE AS *MEMORIALS;* THEY ARE FOR THE REMEMBRANCE OF DIVINE *POWER*. I SEE THE *HOLINESS* OF THE LORD AND HIS SAINTS, AND I AM *SET ON FIRE* TO *IMITATE* THEM ZEALOUSLY.

YEAH, THAT'S WHAT I WAS SAYING... THEY REALLY *HIT* YOU WHERE YOU *LIVE*.

ICONS ARE MADE TO REFLECT THE GLORY OF *GOD* AND THE SAINTS, TO PROMOTE *VIRTUE*, THE AVOIDANCE OF *EVIL* AND THE *SALVATION* OF SOULS. FOR *THIS* REASON WE HONOR THEM.

43

IT IS TRUE, GOD IS *INVISIBLE* AND *INCOMPREHENSIBLE*. BUT JESUS CHRIST IS HIS EXPRESS *IMAGE*, THE *TRUE ICON* OF GOD. WHAT WE DEPICT IN THE ICON IS THE WONDERFUL CONDESCENSION OF GOD'S *INCARNATION*. WE PORTRAY HIS *FACE*, HIS SAVING *ACTIONS*, HIS *SAINTS*...

SURE, I UNDERSTAND THAT THE INCARNATION HAS CHANGED EVERYTHING. BECAUSE THE *SON OF GOD* TOOK ON HUMAN NATURE AND HAD A HUMAN *FACE*, WE CAN *PAINT* HIM. I GUESS FOR ME, THE *BIG* PROBLEM IS THE *SAINTS*.

SAINTS ARE A ...*PROBLEM?*

I MEAN THE WHOLE THING ABOUT *PRAYING* TO SAINTS AND SETTING UP ALL THESE *MEDIATORS* BETWEEN JESUS CHRIST AND THE BELIEVER. KISSING ON ICONS, COUNTING ON THEM TO HAVE MAGICAL *HEALING* POWER, ETC. IT'S A BIG *MESS* OF *SUPERSTITION*, *IDOLATRY* AND *BONDAGE*.

I... I THINK I SEE. YOU SEEM TO BE CONFUSING *VENERATION* WITH *WORSHIP*. GOD *ALONE* IS TO BE WORSHIPED. BUT WE *VENERATE* THE SAINTS, AND GIVE THEM THE *HONOR* THAT IS DUE TO THEM. WHEN WE GIVE HONOR TO THEIR *IMAGES*, THAT HONOR IS REFERRED TO *THEM*.

AND WHEN WE GIVE HONOR TO THE ICON OF JESUS CHRIST, GOD *INCARNATE*, THAT WORSHIP IS *NOT* DIRECTED TO THE PIECE OF PAINTED *BOARD* BUT TO *GOD* ALONE.

WELL, *KISSING* AND *BOWING* JUST SEEMS TO ME LIKE IT CROSSES SOME KIND OF *LINE*.

IT IS ONLY THE *PROPER RESPECT* FOR HOLY THINGS.

WELL, COME TO THINK OF IT, I *WAS* TAUGHT NEVER TO SET ANYTHING DOWN ON TOP OF MY *BIBLE*... BUT I DON'T GO *SMOOCHING* ON IT.

45

MEET THE THEOLOGIANS

JOHN OF DAMASCUS

675-749

WE DON'T KNOW MUCH ABOUT JOHN'S LIFE, BUT SEVERAL FASCINATING LEGENDS HAVE BEEN PRESERVED. ONE OF THE MOST FAMOUS STORIES TELLS OF HOW JOHN WAS FALSELY ACCUSED OF WRITING A SEDITIOUS LETTER AND HAD HIS HAND CUT OFF IN PUNISHMENT. THE AUTHORITIES HUNG THE HAND IN PUBLIC FOR A DAY, THEN GAVE IT BACK TO JOHN, "FOR BURIAL." ACCORDING TO THE STORY, JOHN RE-ATTACHED IT AND PRAYED, AND WOKE UP THE NEXT MORNING ENTIRELY HEALED!

JOHN OF DAMASCUS WAS BORN INTO A WEALTHY CHRISTIAN FAMILY IN DAMASCUS UNDER MOSLEM RULE. HE RECEIVED A VERY GOOD EDUCATION AND WORKED FOR A WHILE AS A TREASURER TO THE CALIPH. HE GAVE UP THIS HIGH-PAYING CAREER TO BECOME A MONK AND A PRIEST. HE CAME TO BE KNOWN AS THE GREATEST SYSTEMATIZER OF THE THEOLOGY OF THE EASTERN CHURCH.

> OH *GOODY!* NOW I CAN FINISH THAT *BOOK* I WAS WORKING ON!

JOHN WAS A HARD-WORKING AND THOROUGH SCHOLAR. FOR EXAMPLE, ONE BOOK HE WROTE CONSISTED OF A LIST OF 103 HERESIES, WHICH HE REFUTED ONE BY ONE. HIS MOST INFLUENTIAL BOOK, ON THE ORTHODOX FAITH, IS A COMPILATION OF THE CHURCH'S TEACHINGS AND THE IDEAS OF THE ANCIENT THEOLOGIANS. JOHN'S GENIUS WAS NOT HIS CREATIVITY BUT HIS ABILITY TO GATHER UP AND SUMMARIZE THE ENTIRE TRADITION THAT HAD GONE BEFORE HIM. HE WAS PROUD OF THE FACT THAT HIS BOOK DID NOT CONTAIN A SINGLE NEW IDEA; IN-TRODUCED NOTHING WHICH HAD NOT BEEN SAID BEFORE! ALTHOUGH HE WAS MUCH MORE THAN JUST A HUMAN COPYING MACHINE, JOHN'S GREAT TALENT WAS HIS ABILITY TO LET THE GRAND CHRISTIAN TRADITION SPEAK THROUGH HIM!

EPIPHANIUS
LEO the GREAT
GREGORY NAZIANZEN
ARISTOTLE
ATHANASIUS
BASIL
DIONYSIUS AREOPAGITE
NEMESIUS
JOHN CHRYSOSTOM
CYRIL OF ALEXANDRIA
MAXIMUS CONFESSOR

> THIS IS REALLY *GREAT* STUFF I'M WRITING, IF I DO SAY SO MYSELF!

JOHN IS ALSO REMEMBERED FOR HIS ROLE IN THE ICON-OCLASTIC CONTROVERSY. EASTERN CHRISTIANS, AND ESPECIALLY THE MONKS, HAD DEVELOPED THE PRACTICE OF WORSHIPING GOD AND HON-ORING SAINTS THROUGH ICONS. WHEN SOME THEOLOGIANS CONDEMNED THIS USE OF IMAGES, JOHN DEFENDED IT. HE ARGUED THAT THE MONKS WERE NOT WORSHIPING THE ICONS --ONLY GOD IS TO BE WORSHIPED-- BUT THEY WERE ONLY GIVING THEM THE HONOR DUE TO THEM AS IMAGES OF SANCTIFICATION.

> DON'T *MESS* WITH THE *MONKS,* MAN!

GOD IS INVISIBLE AND INCOMPREHENSIBLE, JOHN ARGUED, AND THERE IS NO WAY ANYONE COULD EVER MAKE A PICTURE OF GOD. BUT BECAUSE GOD'S SON HAS BECOME INCARNATE IN JESUS CHRIST, HE HAS MADE IT POSSIBLE FOR US TO SEE AND TOUCH HIM. BECAUSE HE HAS COME SO CLOSE TO US, WE CAN DRAW NEAR TO HIM IN HIS VISIBLE, TANGIBLE FORM. GOD HAS GIVEN HIMSELF TO US WITHIN OUR PHYSICAL, SENSORY LIMITS!

> DEPICT HIS WONDER-FUL CONDESCENSION, HIS BIRTH FROM THE VIRGIN, HIS BAPTISM IN THE JORDAN, HIS TRANS-FIGURATION, HIS SUFFER-INGS, HIS PASSION, HIS DEATH... USE EVERY KIND OF DRAWING, WORD OR COLOR. *FEAR NOT;* HAVE NO ANXIETY!

THEO & DEMPFEY'S WORD PAGE

IT'S A *TABULATION* OF *GERMANE LOCUTIONS.*

NO, IT'S IN *ENGLISH.* IT'S JUST A *WORD PAGE!*

LOGOS

THIS IS THE GREEK WORD FOR "WORD." I PRONOUNCE IT *LOW*-GOSS. THE FIRST VERSE OF JOHN'S GOSPEL SAYS, "IN THE BEGINNING WAS THE *LOW*-GOSS."

HEY, THAT'S *NEAT!* SO IF THE STUDY OF *LIFE* IS *BIO*LOGY, THEN IS THE STUDY OF THE WORD *LOGO*LOGY? OR WHAT?

INCARNATION

THIS IS A WORD WHICH MEANS *"BECOMING FLESH."* THE 14TH VERSE OF JOHN'S GOSPEL SAYS, "THE *LOGOS* BECAME *FLESH."* TRANSLATED INTO *LATIN,* THAT WOULD BE *"INCARNATE."*

EVERYTHING'S THE GOSPEL OF JOHN WITH YOU, ISN'T IT?

INSPIRATION

INSPIRATION MEANS *"BREATHED BY GOD."* THE *BIBLE* IS INSPIRED IN A *UNIQUE* WAY, BEING THE VERY *WORD* OF GOD TO US.

SO JESUS IS THE *INCARNATE* WORD OF GOD, AND THE BIBLE IS THE *INSPIRED* WORD OF GOD. HEY, THIS WAS ACTUALLY *HELPFUL!* THANKS, *MR. DICTIONARY!*

The Meadow

> If sheep desire to show their shepherd how much they have eaten, they do so by digesting the pasture internally and producing wool and milk externally. They do not vomit up the grass as a demonstration of their good eating.
> —Epictetus the Stoic

GOOD ADVICE! BUT I STILL THOUGHT YOU MIGHT LIKE TO SEE SOME OF THE STUFF I'VE BEEN **GRAZING** ON, IN CASE YOU WANT TO **RUMINATE** ON SOME OF IT YOURSELF!

THE TEXT OF THE *EPISTLE TO DIOGNETUS* IS MY OWN VERSION; IT'S A PARAPHRASE BASED ON FOUR DIFFERENT ENGLISH TRANSLATIONS AND GLANCES AT THE GREEK ORIGINAL. IT'S AN ABRIDGMENT, AND I LEFT OUT SOME GREAT STUFF, SO GET AHOLD OF THE ORIGINAL AND READ IT! YOU CAN FIND IT IN ANY COLLECTION OF "THE APOSTOLIC FATHERS," WHICH IS THAT SET OF ANCIENT CHRISTIAN WRITINGS THAT APPEARED SHORTLY AFTER THE APOSTLES. THE OLD-TIMEY PICTURES IN THE "HERE COMES A GREAT BIG APOLOGY" ARE FROM TWO PLACES: HARTER'S PICTURE ARCHIVE (NY: DOVER BOOKS, 1978) AND GUSTAVE DORÉ'S ILLUSTRATIONS OF THE BIBLE.

THE TEXT OF ATHANASIUS' *ON THE INCARNATION* IS ALSO MY OWN PARAPHRASE, BASED ON THREE ENGLISH TRANSLATIONS. THANKS TO JOHN WEHLING FOR PROOFREADING IT FOR ME AND CATCHING A COUPLE OF OMISSIONS. YOU SHOULD DEFINITELY GO READ THE WHOLE BOOK, BECAUSE THIS VERSION IS JUST THE HIGHLIGHTS. TRY TO FIND THE LITTLE PAPERBACK EDITION WITH AN INTRODUCTION BY C.S. LEWIS (IT WAS ONE OF HIS FAVORITE BOOKS). FOR A FUN DRAMATIZATION OF THE COUNCIL OF NICEA, WITH ATHANASIUS AS THE HERO, READ DOROTHY SAYERS' PLAY *THE EMPEROR CONSTANTINE*. THE BIG PICTURES BEHIND ATHANASIUS ARE ADAPTED FROM NICHOLAS OF VERDUN'S KOSTERNEUBERG ALTAR, A BEAUTIFUL WORK IN ENAMEL. MY CARTOON OF ATHANASIUS IS BASED ON A MOSAIC IN THE CAPELLA PALATINA IN PALERMO, ITALY.

THE CHAPTER ON SCRIPTURE IS BASED ON A LOT OF STUDYING, BUT THE WRITERS I CAN RECOMMEND MOST WOULD BE JOHN GOLDINGAY AND DONALD BLOESCH, AND FURTHER BACK J.A. BENGEL AND KARL BARTH. I GOT A LOT OF HELP FROM JOHN WEHLING AND JOE HENDERSON IN TALKING ABOUT THE IDEAS INVOLVED, AND AFTER THE FACT I HAD A GOOD EXCHANGE WITH RON AND KRIS CREASMAN ABOUT IT.

CLICKING ON ICONS WAS ORIGINALLY A PAMPHLET WHICH ACCOMPANIED AN EXHIBIT AT THE GRADUATE THEOLOGICAL UNION LIBRARY: "THE VISIBLE WORD," CURATED BY KEVIN KOCZELA AND EUGENE LUDWIG. SPECIAL THANKS TO KEVIN FOR ORGANIZING THE SHOW, SUGGESTING THE COMIC, AND HELPING ME FIGURE OUT WHAT JOHN OF DAMASCUS WOULD HAVE TO SAY. THE TEXT IS A PARAPHRASE OF JOHN'S "APOLOGY AGAINST THOSE WHO ATTACK THE DIVINE IMAGES." FOR READING ABOUT ICONS I RECOMMEND LEONID OUSPENSKY AND VLADIMIR LOSSKY'S BOOK *THE MEANING OF ICONS*.

--FRED SANDERS